NELSON

Math

GRADE
K

NELSON

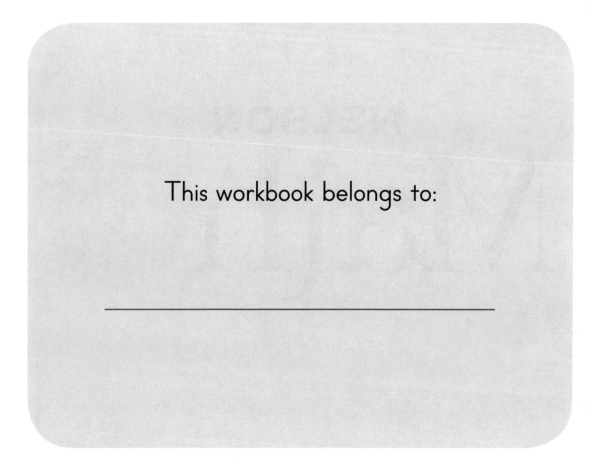

This workbook belongs to:

_____

NELSON

COPYRIGHT © 2018 by Nelson Education Ltd.

ISBN-13: 978-0-17-684826-2
ISBN-10: 0-17-684826-6

Printed and bound in Canada
1 2 3 4   21 20 19 18

For more information contact Nelson Education Ltd.,
1120 Birchmount Road, Toronto, Ontario M1K 5G4. Or you
can visit our website at nelson.com.

Contents

REWARD CONTRACT

When you complete a topic in your Nelson Math Workbook, colour in a circle.

START

Numbers

Measurement

Geometry

Patterns

Data Management

FINISH

Name: _____ Date: _____

My reward will be: _____

Parent/Guardian: _____

Reading 1 to 5

Read the numbers. Match each number with the same number of fingers.

1

2

3

4

5

Printing Numbers: 1

There is 1 tractor.

Trace and print the number 1.

LEARNING TIPS

The small dot indicates where your child should start tracing the number.

Printing Numbers: 2

There are 2 boats.

Trace and print the number 2.

2 2 2 2 2 2 2 2 2

LEARNING TIPS

Encourage your child to first practise writing the numbers in the air with his or her finger. If your child needs more practice tracing to establish the number shape, you can write the numbers in dashed lines.

Printing Numbers: 3

There are 3 scooters.

Trace and print the number 3.

3 3 3 3 3 3

LEARNING TIPS

Children can form numbers and letters more easily when gripping the pencil properly. Consider putting a slide-on pencil grip on your child's pencil to position his or her fingers properly.

Printing Numbers: 4

There are 4 bikes.

Trace and print the number 4.

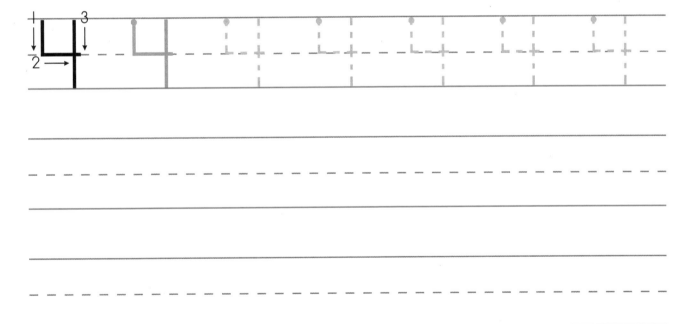

LEARNING TIPS

Encourage your child to print numbers using the steps shown with arrows.

Printing Numbers: 5

There are 5 cars.

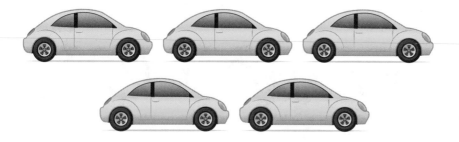

Trace and print the number 5.

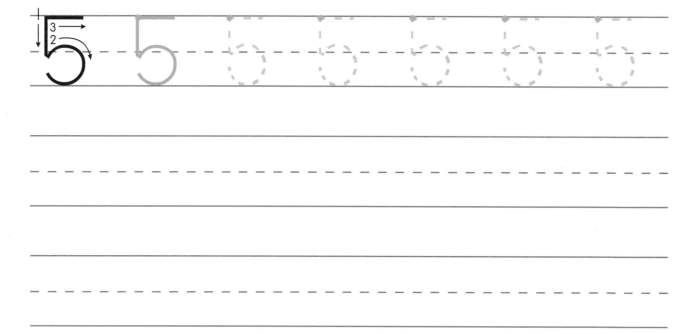

LEARNING TIPS

Your child may benefit from using a short pencil, such as a golf pencil, to write. Since children cannot easily grab a short pencil in their fists, it encourages them to use a proper pencil grip.

Printing Numbers: 0

There are no fish in the fish bowl.

You can say there are zero fish.

Trace and print the number 0.

LEARNING TIPS

Help your child distinguish the number 0 from the letter "O." A zero is more oval-shaped.

Representing Numbers to 5

1. Selah has 5 buttons.

She showed 5 on a 5-frame.

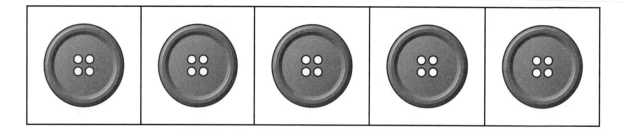

Show 4 on this 5-frame. You can draw dots or use buttons, coins, or other counters.

2. Leah has 3 crayons. She coloured the number path to show 3.

1	2	3	4	5

Colour the number path to show 5.

1	2	3	4	5

Colour the number path to show 2.

1	2	3	4	5

Recognizing Quantities

1. Match each number to the die with the same number of dots.

3

2

4

5

1

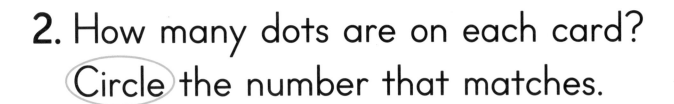

2. How many dots are on each card? Circle the number that matches.

   1 2 3 4 5

   1 2 3 4 5

   1 2 3 4 5

   1 2 3 4 5

   1 2 3 4 5

   1 2 3 4 5

   1 2 3 4 5

Counting to 5

1. Number the last coin in each group. Write the total number of coins in each group.

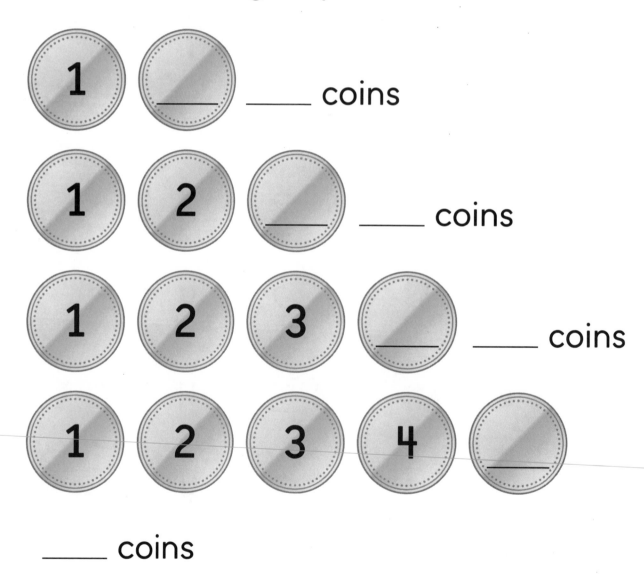

1 ___ ___ coins

1 2 ___ ___ coins

1 2 3 ___ ___ coins

1 2 3 4 ___

___ coins

2. Write the missing numbers below the trains.

1   2   ____

____   2   3   ____

1   ____   3   4   ____

LEARNING TIPS

The last number counted will tell your child how many items there are in total.
Help your child understand that number order never changes.

Reading 6 to 10

Match each number with the same number of fruit.

6

7

8

9

10

Printing Numbers: 6

There are 6 butterflies.

Trace and print the number 6.

6   6   6   6   6   6   6

LEARNING TIPS

The number 6, as well as other curved numbers such as 8, should be drawn in one fluid line.

Printing Numbers: 7

There are 7 ladybugs.

Trace and print the number 7.

Printing Numbers: 8

There are 8 snails.

Trace and print the number 8.

8 8 8 8 8 8 8

LEARNING TIPS

Other writing activities can strengthen pencil grip and provide practice with pencil strokes that help when printing numbers. For example, your child can do mazes, complete connect-the-dot pictures, and colour.

Printing Numbers: 9

There are 9 leaves.

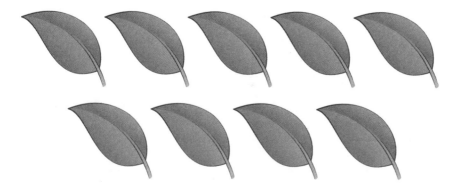

LEARNING TIPS

Each time your child prints the number 9, have him or her say the word "nine" to connect the word with the number.

Trace and print the number 9.

Printing Numbers: 10

There are 10 stars.

Trace and print the number 10.

Representing Numbers to 10

1. Lucas collected some rocks.
To help count them, he put them on a 10-frame.

How many rocks does he have?

_____

2. Show 7 on the 10-frame.

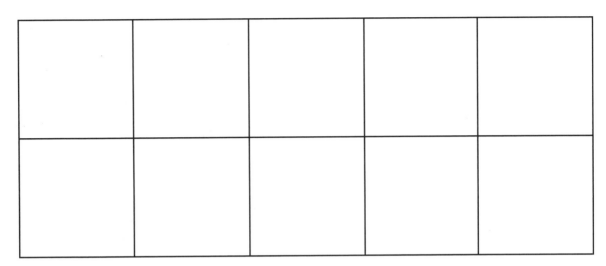

3. Show 6 on the 10-frame.

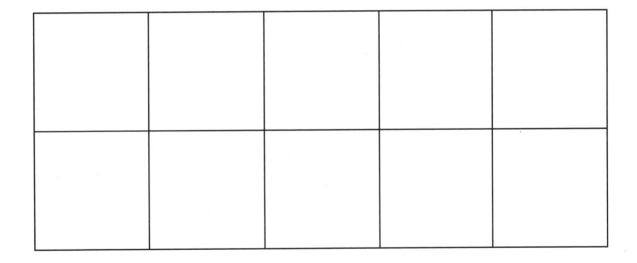

4. Show 9. Colour the squares on the number path.

| 1 | 2 | 3 | 4 | 5 | 6 | 7 | 8 | 9 | 10 |

Counting to 10

1. What is this mystery animal? Join the dots in order from 1 to 10.

2. Fill in the missing numbers on each caterpillar.

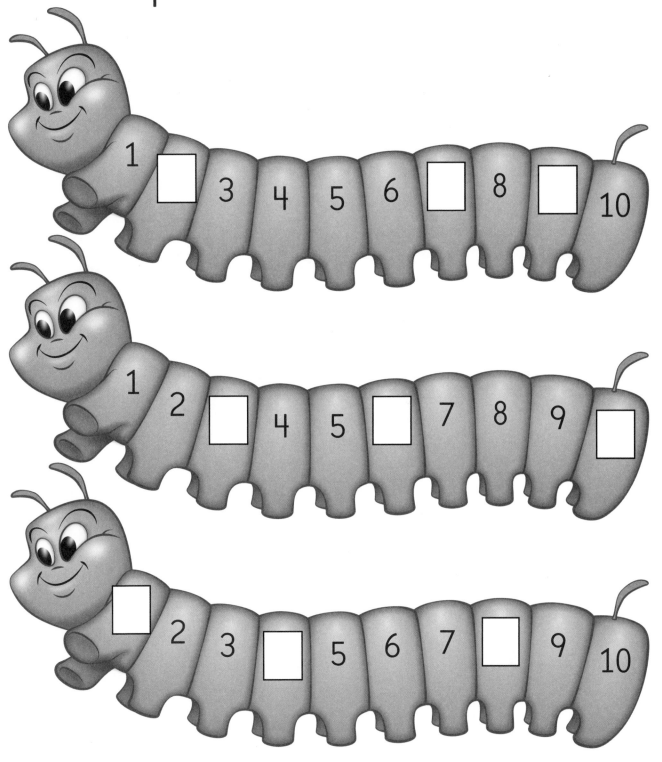

Keeping Track When Counting

1. Time to clean up! Count how many toys need to be put away. Circle the number that matches.

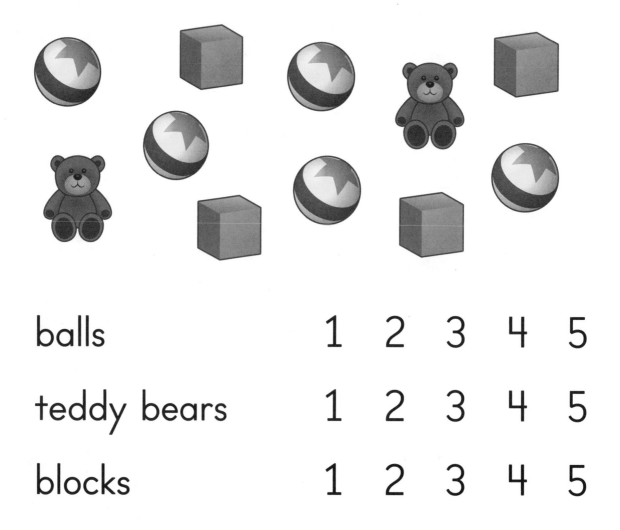

balls	1	2	3	4	5
teddy bears	1	2	3	4	5
blocks	1	2	3	4	5

2. Count how many of each fruit there is. Write the number.

apples _____

bananas _____

oranges _____

What Has More?

1. Count the bubbles. Write the number. Circle the group that has **more** bubbles.

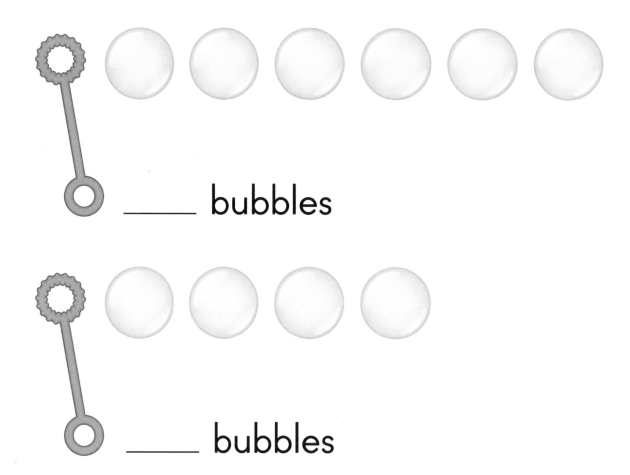

_____ bubbles

_____ bubbles

LEARNING TIPS

When comparing two quantities, **more** indicates the quantity or group with a greater number of objects. Remind your child that the last number counted represents the number of objects in the set.

2. Count the boats in each group. Write the number. (Circle) the group that has more boats.

_____ boats   _____ boats

_____ boats   _____ boat

Which Has Fewer?

1. Count the beads on each string. Write the number. Circle the string that has **fewer** beads.

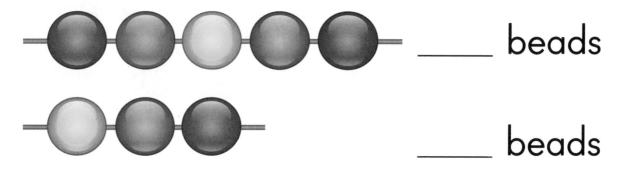

_____ beads

_____ beads

_____ beads

_____ bead

LEARNING TIPS

When comparing two quantities, **fewer** indicates the quantity or group with a smaller number of objects.

2. Count the scoops on each cone.
Write the number. Circle the cone
that has fewer scoops.

_____ scoops   _____ scoops

_____ scoops   _____ scoops

Numbers   29

More or Fewer?

1. Make pairs. Draw a line to match bunnies and carrots.

(Circle) the group with more.

bunnies   carrots

LEARNING TIPS

Remind your child that words like "bigger" and "smaller" describe differences in the sizes of objects. Words like "more," "fewer," and "less" refer to the number of objects.

2. Make pairs. Draw a line to match shovels and buckets.

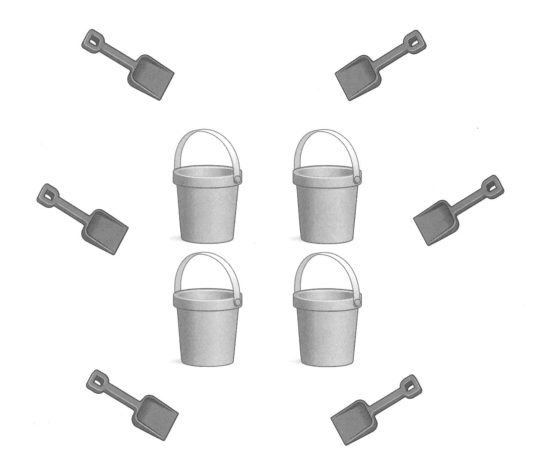

Circle the group with fewer.

buckets

shovels

Comparing Big and Small Objects

1. Write the number of each fruit.
Circle the row that has more fruit.

_____ watermelons

_____ apples

LEARNING TIPS

If needed, point out the difference between the number of objects in a group and the physical size of the objects.

2. Circle the group that has more objects.

3. Circle the group that has fewer objects.

Matching Equal Groups

1. Match the groups with the same number of objects.

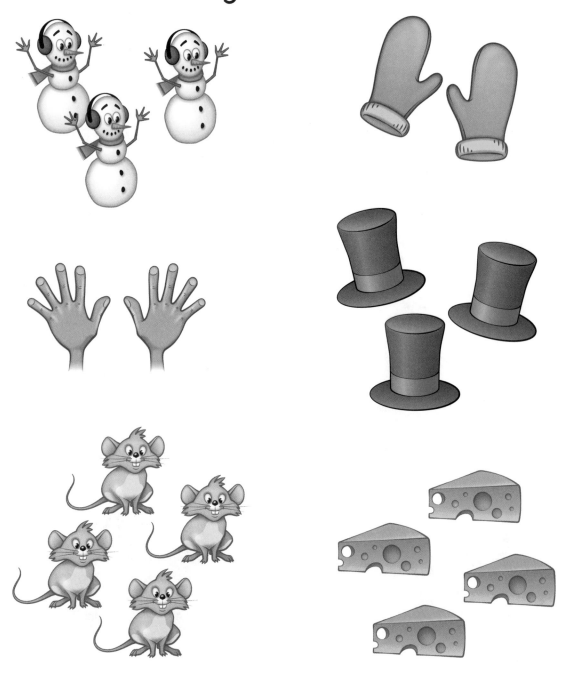

2. Count the red hats.
Write the number in the box.

Make the same number of blue hats and red hats.
Cross out blue hats.

Which Number Is Greater?

Kyrie finds 7 rocks. Colour in the number path to show 7.

1	2	3	4	5	6	7	8	9	10

Allie finds 3 rocks. Colour in the number path to show 3.

1	2	3	4	5	6	7	8	9	10

Circle the greater number.

7   3

LEARNING TIPS

Help your child understand that quantity is greater when counting forward and smaller when counting backward.

Ordinal Numbers

The train has 5 cars.

How many windows does the second car have? _____

How many windows does the third car have? _____

Draw an X on the fourth car.

Circle the fifth car.

LEARNING TIPS

Ordinal numbers (for example, first, second, third) show the order of something in a list or a sequence.

Coins

1. Match each coin to its name.

dime

quarter

loonie

nickel

2. How much is each coin worth?
Circle the value.

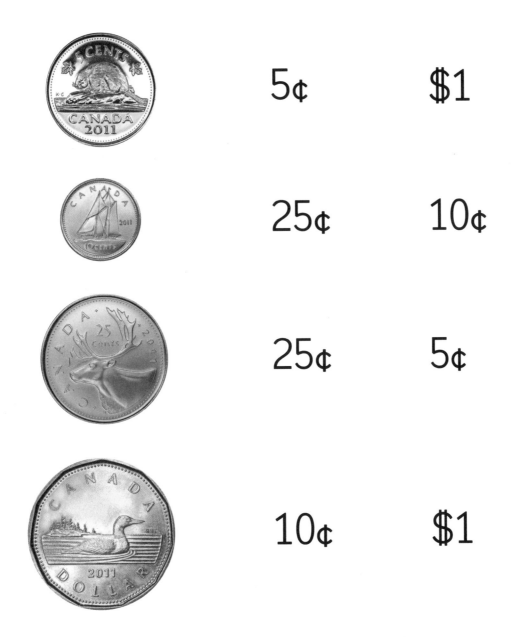

5¢ $1

25¢   10¢

25¢   5¢

10¢ $1

Taking Numbers Apart

There are 6 apples in a basket. Some are red. Some are yellow.

1. Colour the apples. Show how many are red and how many are yellow.

How many apples are red? _____

How many apples are yellow? _____

How many apples are there altogether? _____

2. Colour the apples a different way. Show how many are red and how many are yellow.

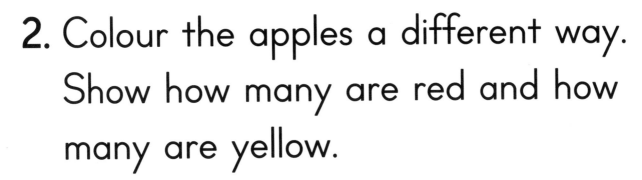

How many apples are red? ——

How many apples are yellow? ——

How many apples are there altogether? ——

LEARNING TIPS

Your child may need extra practice understanding how numbers can be broken into two parts in several ways. You can replicate these activities using real objects, such as blocks. Have your child build two structures using the same number of blocks but with different colour combinations.

Putting Numbers Together

1. Count the total number of dots on each domino. Write the number below the domino.

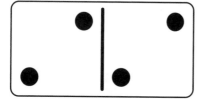

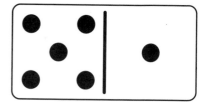

_____

_____

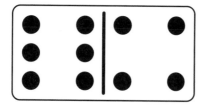

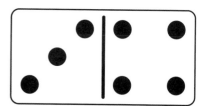

_____

_____

2. Look at the numbers below each domino. Draw dots on both sides of the domino to make the number.

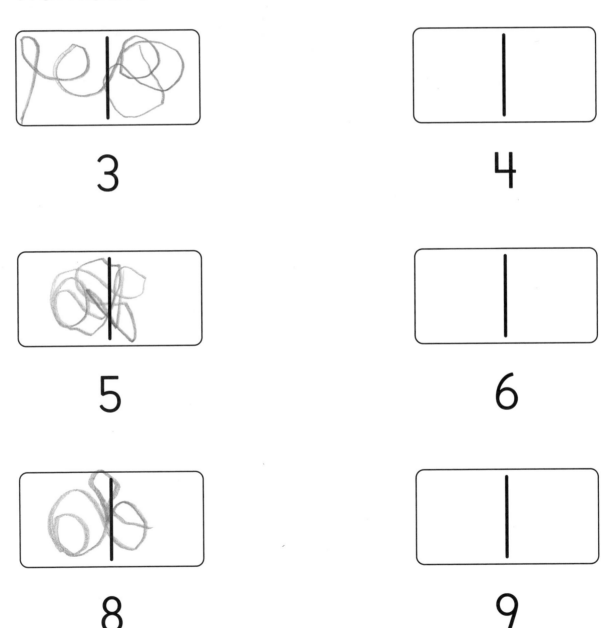

3

4

5

6

8

9

Addition: 1 or 2 More

1. There are 4 frogs.

1 more frog comes along.

How many frogs are on the log now? _____

2. There are 6 fish.

2 more fish come along.

How many fish are there now?

_____

Joining Groups

1. Sophie bakes 2 pies.

James bakes 3 pies.

How many pies are there altogether? _____

LEARNING TIPS

Help your child understand that even if objects aren't identical, they can be counted together as a group.

2. Henry has 5 blue marbles.

Sam has 3 green marbles.

How many marbles do they have altogether? _____

Subtraction: 1 or 2 Less

1. There are 4 birds on a branch.

1 bird flew away.

How many birds are on the branch now? _____

2. There are 10 cookies.

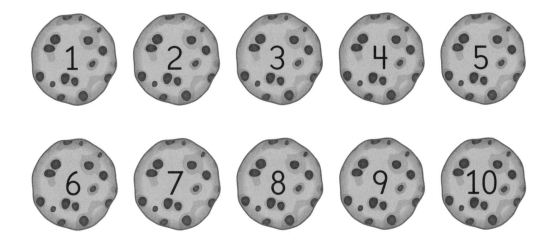

Mark ate 2 cookies.

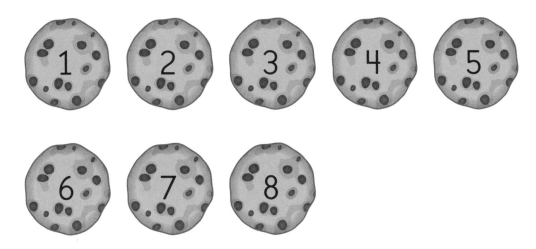

How many cookies are there now?

_____

Taking Groups Away

1. Gabriel has 6 cupcakes.

His friends eat the 3 blue cupcakes. Mark an X on the cupcakes his friends eat.

How many cupcakes are left? _____

2. Stella has 8 glasses of lemonade.

She sells the 5 glasses with lemon slices. Mark an X on the 5 glasses she sold.

How many glasses does she have left? ____

Test Yourself

1. Write the number of objects in each group.

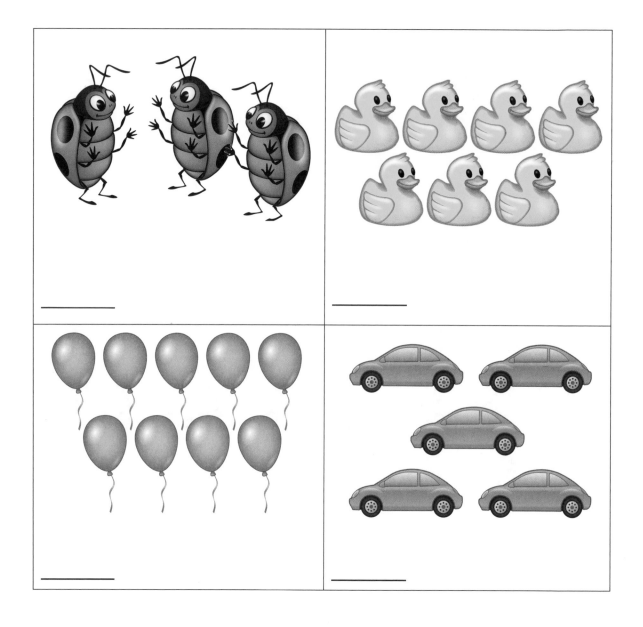

2. There are 3 blue hats and 2 red hats. How many hats are there altogether? ____

3. Olivia has 6 star stickers. She gives 2 stickers away. How many stickers does she have left? ____

Comparing Length

1. (Circle) the **longer** carrot.

2. (Circle) **shorter** fish.

LEARNING TIPS

Longer and **shorter** are measuring terms used when comparing length. An object with a greater length is longer. An object with a smaller length is shorter.

Ordering by Length

Number the snakes. Put them in order from shortest to longest.

The shortest will be 1.

The longest will be 3.

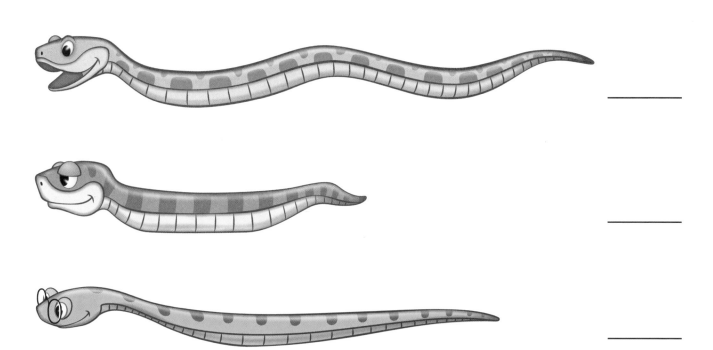

_____

_____

_____

LEARNING TIPS

Your child can use his or her thumb and index finger to compare lengths of different objects.

Comparing Heights

1. Circle the taller giraffe.

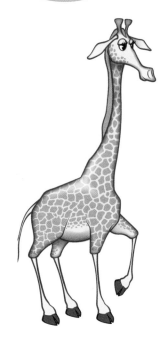

2. Circle the shorter bottle.

Ordering by Height

Number the trees. Put them in order from shortest to tallest.

The shortest will be 1.

The tallest will be 3.

_____   _____   _____

LEARNING TIPS

Tools such as pieces of string can be used to
help compare heights or lengths of objects.

Measuring Length

1. How many snap cubes long is the caterpillar?

_____ snap cubes long

2. How many paper clips long is the pencil crayon?

_____ paper clips long

LEARNING TIPS

Nonstandard units, such as blocks and paper clips, can be used to measure an object's length. Nonstandard units should be the same size and lined up end to end.

Measuring Height

1. How many blocks tall is the glass?

_____ blocks tall

2. How many snap cubes tall is the flower?

_____ snap cubes tall

LEARNING TIPS

To make measuring more precise, draw lines marking the bottom and top of the object.

Mass

1. Circle the heavier object.

2. Circle the lighter object.

LEARNING TIPS

Encourage your child to compare the **mass** of different objects by holding them. Ask them to tell you which one they think is heavier, and then have them hold the objects to see if they are correct.

Capacity

1. Circle the cup that holds the most.

2. Circle the pot that holds the least.

LEARNING TIPS

Encourage your child to explore the **capacity** of different containers. For example, ask, "Do you think this glass will hold less water than the pitcher? How can we find out?"

Test Yourself

1. (Circle) the longer bus.

2. (Circle) the shorter ladder.

3. Circle the heavier animal.

4. Circle the cup that holds the most.

Measurement 63

Circles

1. Colour each shape that is a **circle**.

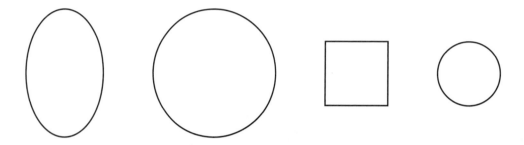

2. Circle the objects with circles in them.

LEARNING TIPS

Children sometimes think that ovals are circles. Help your child understand that **circles** are perfectly round.

Squares

1. Colour each shape that is a **square**.

 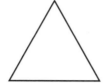 

2. Circle the objects with squares in them.

LEARNING TIPS

Squares have four sides of equal length.

Triangles

1. Colour each shape that is a **triangle**.

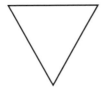   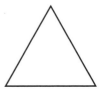

2. Circle the objects with triangles in them.

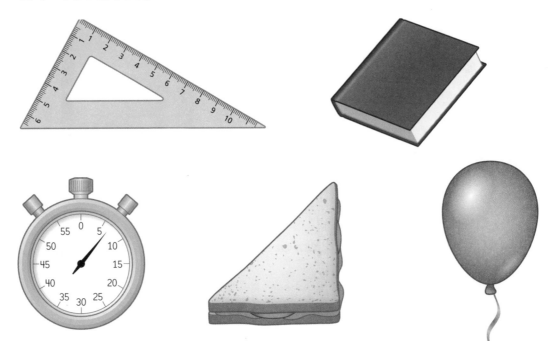

LEARNING TIPS

Triangles always have three sides. Remind your child that two triangles can look different but still both be triangles.

Rectangles

1. Colour each shape that is a **rectangle**.

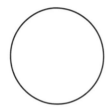   

2. Circle the objects with rectangles in them.

LEARNING TIPS

Rectangles have four sides, like squares, but two sides are longer than the other two sides.

Drawing Shapes

Trace the shape.
Circle the shape name.

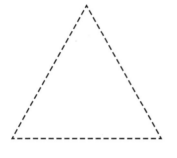

triangle   or   square

rectangle   or   circle

triangle   or   circle

square   or   triangle

Taking Shapes Apart

How many new shapes are being made? Fill in the blanks.

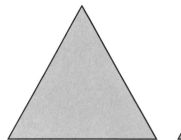 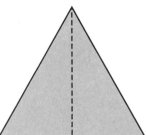 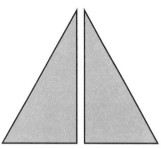

1 triangle can make ____ smaller triangles.

 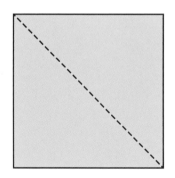 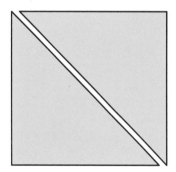

1 square can make ____ smaller triangles.

Number of Sides

1. Write the number of **sides** each shape has.

Shape	Number of sides

LEARNING TIPS

A **side** is a straight line that joins two corners of a shape.

2. Colour the shapes with 4 sides green. Colour the shapes with 3 sides blue.

Number of Corners

1. Write the number of **corners** each shape has.

Shape	Number of corners

LEARNING TIPS

A **corner** is a point where two lines (sides) meet. For example, a square has 4 corners.

2. Colour the shapes with 4 corners red. Colour the shapes with 3 corners purple.

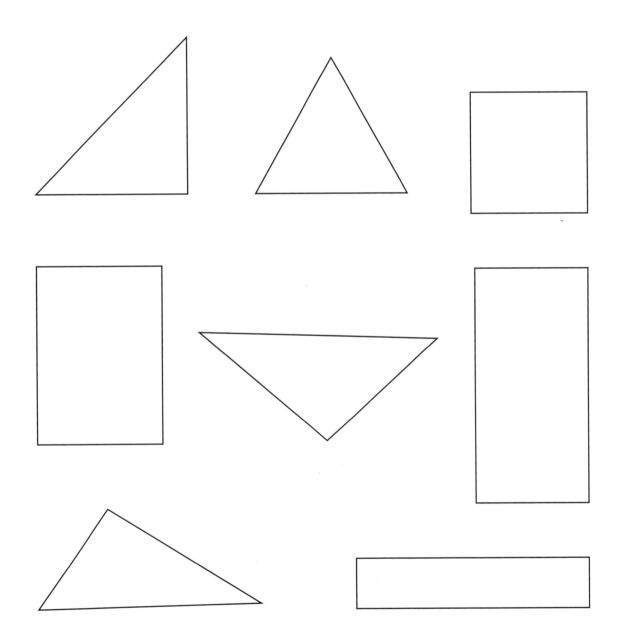

Ball Shapes

1. (Circle) the **ball shapes**.

2. (Circle) the objects that are ball shapes.

LEARNING TIPS

Ball shapes are perfectly round 3-D objects that are shaped like balls. Circles are flat 2-D shapes.

Box Shapes

1. (Circle) the **box shapes.**

2. (Circle) the objects that are box shapes.

LEARNING TIPS

Box shapes are 3-D objects that are shaped like a box. A box shape has 6 surfaces that are squares or rectangles.

Can Shapes

1. (Circle) the **can shapes**.

2. (Circle) the objects that are can shapes.

Cones

1. Circle the **cones**.

2. Circle the objects that are cones.

Slide, Stack, and Roll

1. Circle the objects that can **slide**.

2. Circle the objects that can **stack**.

3. Circle the objects that can **roll**.

LEARNING TIPS

Objects that can **slide** have a flat surface. Objects that can **stack** have flat surfaces on the top and bottom, and must not have points (as cones do). Objects that can **roll** have a curved surface.

2-D Shapes and 3-D Objects

Circle the 3-D object that is made
from the 2-D shape.

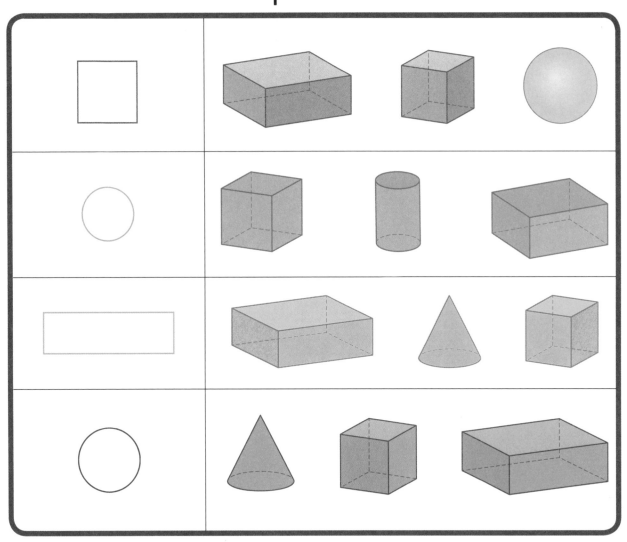

LEARNING TIPS

Have your child trace the surfaces of different 3-D objects in
your house to see what 2-D shapes they are made of.

Above and Below

Is the airplane **above** or **below** the cloud? Circle the answer.

above   below

above   below

LEARNING TIPS

Separating objects with a line can help determine where they are. **Above** means on top of. **Below** means under.

In and Out

Is the fruit **in** or **out** of the basket? Circle the answer.

in   out

in   out

in   out

LEARNING TIPS

In means to be inside or contained by something (in the kitchen). **Out** means to be outside or beyond something (out of the house). In and out are opposites.

Test Yourself

1. Colour the circles red, the squares blue, the triangles orange, and the rectangles purple.

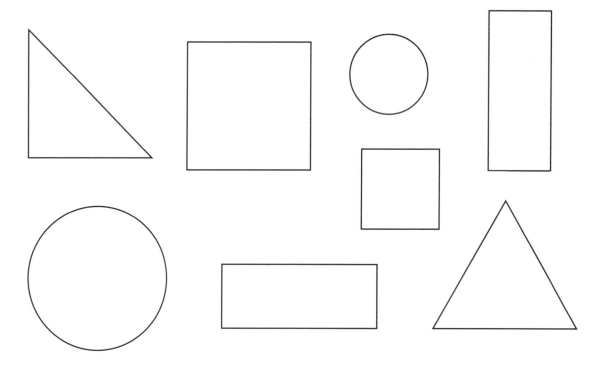

2. Circle the shapes with 4 sides.

3. Colour the ball shape green, the box shape blue, the can shape red, and the cone orange.

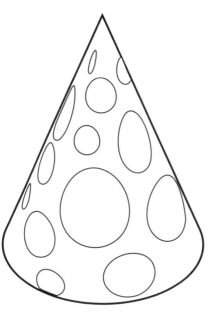

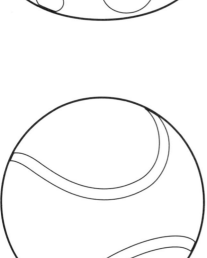

What Comes Next?

1. Circle what comes next in each pattern.

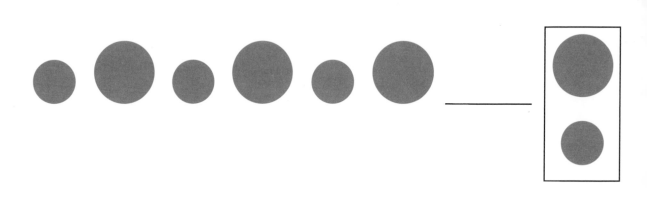

2. Circle what comes next in each pattern.

LEARNING TIPS

Encourage your child to say the name of each shape or object in the pattern. Then he or she can figure out what comes next.

Understanding Patterns

1. Circle the part of the pattern that repeats.

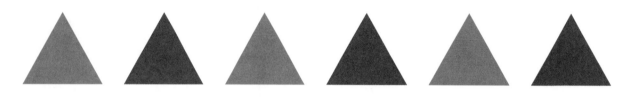

LEARNING TIPS

If your child needs help drawing the shapes, ask him or her to name the shapes.
Then you can draw them in dotted lines, and your child can trace and colour them.

2. Circle the part of the pattern that repeats.

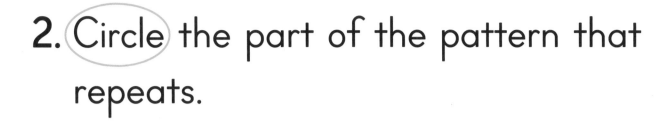

Draw the next 2 shapes in the pattern. Colour the shapes.

3. Circle the part of the pattern that repeats. Draw and colour the next 2 shapes.

Showing Patterns

This is an AB pattern.

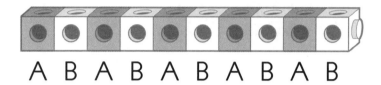

A B A B A B A B A B

Use the letters AB or ABC to show each pattern.

___ ___ ___ ___ ___ ___

___ ___ ___ ___ ___ ___ ___ ___ ___

LEARNING TIPS

Create your own repeating patterns with sounds or actions, and have your child copy the pattern. Encourage your child to describe each pattern using letters, such as AB, ABB, or ABC.

Creating Patterns

Colour the objects to show patterns that repeat.

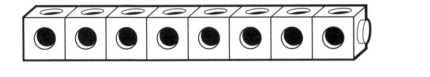

Draw a pattern using different shapes. Repeat the pattern 3 times.

Test Yourself

1. Circle what comes next.

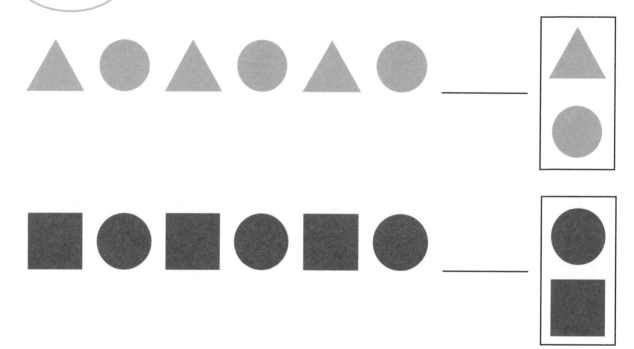

2. Circle the part of the pattern that repeats. Draw and colour the next 2 shapes.

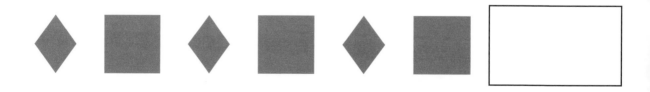

3. Colour the objects to show patterns that repeat.

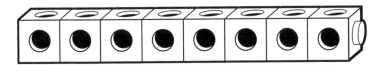

4. Draw your own pattern with shapes. Make the pattern repeat 3 times.

Sorting by Colour

Sort the objects by colour.

Circle the red objects. Draw a box around the blue objects.

Sorting by Size

Sort the shapes by size.

Circle each small object. Write an X on the large objects.

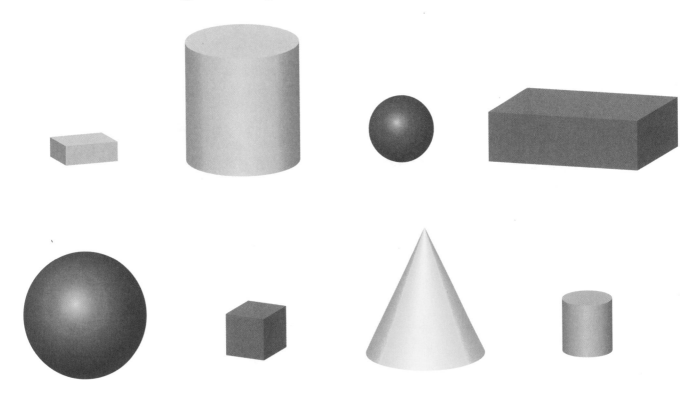

LEARNING TIPS

Ask your child if he or she can sort the 3-D objects above in a different way.
For example, he or she might want to sort by colour or type of shape.

Which Is Different?

1. Circle the object that is different.

   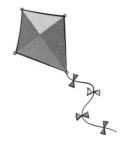

LEARNING TIPS

Have your child explain his or her thinking about how the objects were sorted.

2. Write an X on the object that does not belong.

Collecting Data

1. Sort the hats. How many are there of each? Fill in the table.

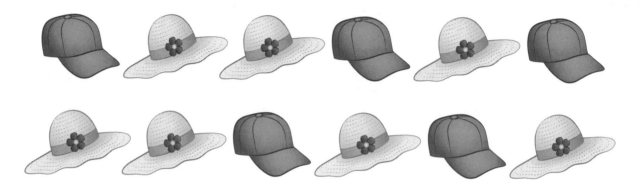

How Many Hats Are There?

Hat	Number of hats

2. Ask friends and family this question: Do you like winter?

Record their answers in this chart.

Do You Like Winter?

Answer	Number of people
I like winter. 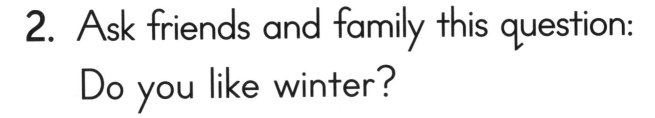	
I don't like winter.	

Picture Graphs

1. Ralph sorted his fruit on this **picture graph**.

Ralph's Fruit

How many strawberries does Ralph have? ____

How many bananas does Ralph have? ____

Circle the fruit that Ralph has more of.

2. This picture graph shows Phuong's friends' favourite colours.

What is Your Favourite Colour?

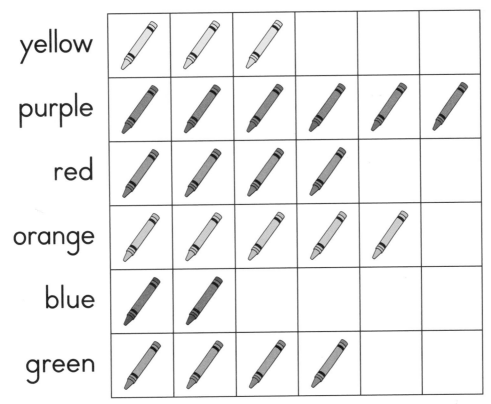

Mark an X on the least favourite colour. (Circle) the favourite colour.

Test Yourself

1. Sort the shapes by colour.
   Fill in the table.

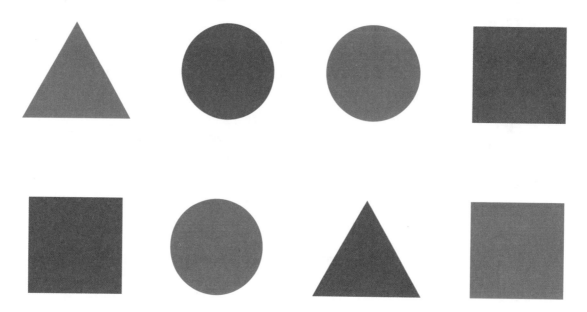

Colour	Number of shapes
Red	
Blue	

2. Subira asked her friends about their favourite pets.

Favourite Pets

cats	🐱	🐱	🐱	🐱	🐱	🐱		
dogs	🐶	🐶	🐶	🐶				

How many people like cats? _____

How many people like dogs? _____

Do more people like cats or dogs? Circle the answer.

Glossary

Above: to be on top of.

Ball shape: a perfectly round 3-D object that is shaped like a ball.

Below: to be under.

Box shape: a 3-D object that is shaped like a box. A box shape has 6 surfaces that are squares or rectangles.

Can shape: a 3-D object that is shaped like a can. It has a circular surfaces on both ends and a curved side.

Capacity: a measure of how much a container can hold.

Circle: a 2-D shape that is perfectly round.

Cone: a 3-D object that has one circular surface and a curved side that comes to a point at the top.

Corner: a point where two lines (sides) of a shape meet.

Fewer: when comparing two quantities, "fewer" indicates the quantity or group with a smaller number of objects.

In: to be inside or contained by something (for example, in the kitchen).

Longer: when comparing the lengths of two objects, the object with a greater length is longer.

Mass: a measure of how much something weighs.

More: when comparing two quantities, "more" indicates the quantity or group with a greater number of objects.

Ordinal numbers: numbers that show the order of something in a list or a sequence (for example, first, second, third).

Out: to be outside or beyond something (for example, out of the house).

Picture graph: a way of showing data using images. Each image stands for 1 thing.

Rectangle: a 2-D shape that has four sides, like a square, but two sides are longer than the other two sides.

Roll: objects that can roll have a curved surface.

Shorter: when comparing the lengths of two objects, the object with a smaller length is shorter.

Side: a straight line that joins two corners of a shape.

Slide: objects that can slide have a flat surface.

Square: a 2-D shape that has four sides of equal length.

Stack: objects that can stack have flat surfaces on the top and bottom, and must not have points (as cones do).

Triangle: a 2-D shape with three sides.

Answers

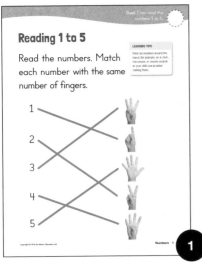

Reading 1 to 5

Read the numbers. Match each number with the same number of fingers.

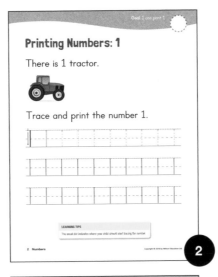

Printing Numbers: 1

There is 1 tractor.

Trace and print the number 1.

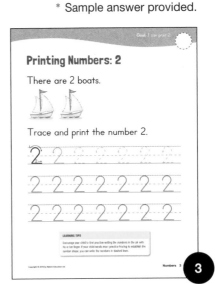

Printing Numbers: 2

There are 2 boats.

Trace and print the number 2.

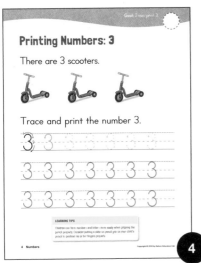

Printing Numbers: 3

There are 3 scooters.

Trace and print the number 3.

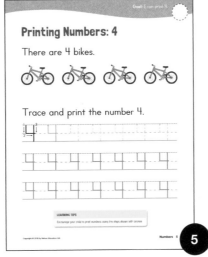

Printing Numbers: 4

There are 4 bikes.

Trace and print the number 4.

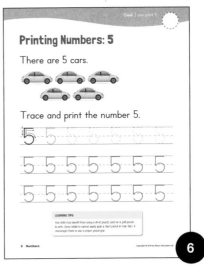

Printing Numbers: 5

There are 5 cars.

Trace and print the number 5.

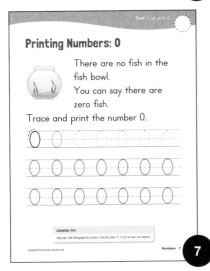

Printing Numbers: 0

There are no fish in the fish bowl.
You can say there are zero fish.
Trace and print the number 0.

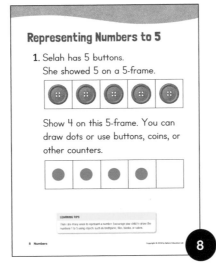

Representing Numbers to 5

1. Selah has 5 buttons.
She showed 5 on a 5-frame.

Show 4 on this 5-frame. You can draw dots or use buttons, coins, or other counters.

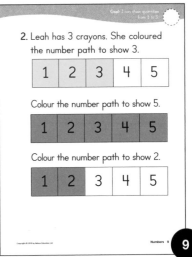

2. Leah has 3 crayons. She coloured the number path to show 3.

| 1 | 2 | 3 | 4 | 5 |

Colour the number path to show 5.

| 1 | 2 | 3 | 4 | 5 |

Colour the number path to show 2.

| 1 | 2 | 3 | 4 | 5 |

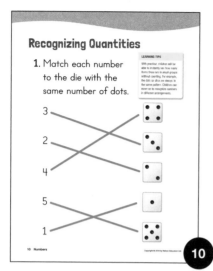

Recognizing Quantities

1. Match each number to the die with the same number of dots.

LEARNING TIPS
With practice, children will be able to instantly see how many items there are in small groups without counting. For example, the dots on dice are always in the same pattern. Children can even go to recognize numbers in different arrangements.

3
2
4
5
1

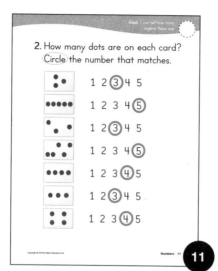

2. How many dots are on each card? Circle the number that matches.

1 2 ③ 4 5
1 2 3 4 ⑤
1 2 ③ 4 5
1 2 3 4 ⑤
1 2 3 ④ 5
1 2 ③ 4 5
1 2 3 ④ 5

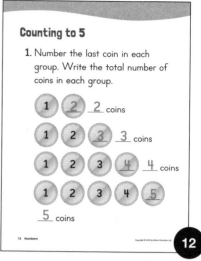

Counting to 5

1. Number the last coin in each group. Write the total number of coins in each group.

1 2 __2__ coins

1 2 3 __3__ coins

1 2 3 4 __4__ coins

1 2 3 4 5 __5__ coins

__5__ coins

2. Write the missing numbers below the trains.

1 2 __3__

__1__ 2 3 __4__

1 __2__ 3 4 __5__

LEARNING TIPS
The last number counted will tell your child how many items there are in total. Help your child understand that number order never changes.

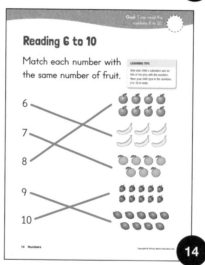

Reading 6 to 10

Match each number with the same number of fruit.

LEARNING TIPS
Give your child a calculator and let him or her play with the numbers. Have your child type in the numbers 6 to 10 in order.

6
7
8
9
10

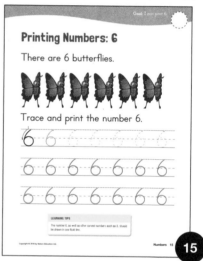

Printing Numbers: 6

There are 6 butterflies.

Trace and print the number 6.

6 6 6 6 6 6 6
6 6 6 6 6 6 6

LEARNING TIPS
The number 6, as well as other curved numbers such as 8, should be drawn in one fluid line.

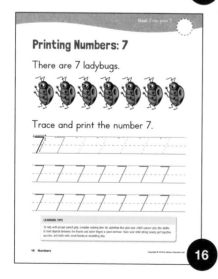

Printing Numbers: 7

There are 7 ladybugs.

Trace and print the number 7.

7 7 7 7 7 7 7
7 7 7 7 7 7 7

LEARNING TIPS
To help with proper pencil grip, consider making time for activities that give your child's proper grip (the ability to hold objects between the thumb and index finger) a good workout. Have your child string beads, put together puzzles, and build with small blocks or modelling clay.

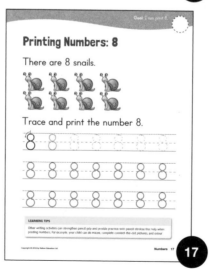

Printing Numbers: 8

There are 8 snails.

Trace and print the number 8.

8 8 8 8 8 8 8
8 8 8 8 8 8 8

LEARNING TIPS
Other writing activities can strengthen pencil grip and provide practice with pencil strokes that help when printing numbers. For example, your child can do mazes, complete connect-the-dot pictures, and colour.

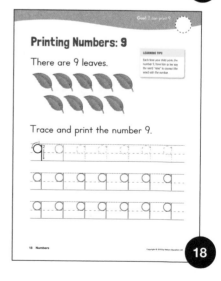

Printing Numbers: 9

There are 9 leaves.

LEARNING TIPS
Each time your child prints the number 9, have him or her say the word "nine" to connect the word with the number.

Trace and print the number 9.

9 9 9 9 9 9 9
9 9 9 9 9 9 9

* Sample answer provided.

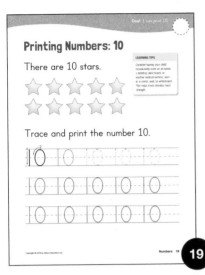

Printing Numbers: 10

There are 10 stars.

Trace and print the number 10.

19

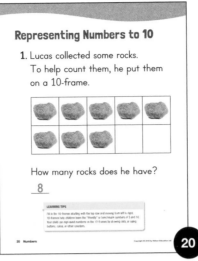

Representing Numbers to 10

1. Lucas collected some rocks. To help count them, he put them on a 10-frame.

How many rocks does he have?

8

20

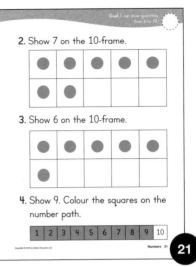

2. Show 7 on the 10-frame.

3. Show 6 on the 10-frame.

4. Show 9. Colour the squares on the number path.

| 1 | 2 | 3 | 4 | 5 | 6 | 7 | 8 | 9 | 10 |

21

Counting to 10

1. What is this mystery animal? Join the dots in order from 1 to 10.

22

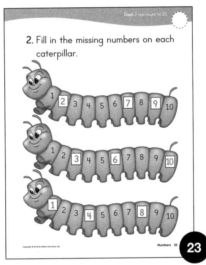

2. Fill in the missing numbers on each caterpillar.

23

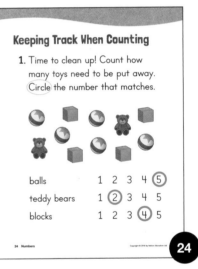

Keeping Track When Counting

1. Time to clean up! Count how many toys need to be put away. Circle the number that matches.

balls   1 2 3 4 ⑤
teddy bears 1 ② 3 4 5
blocks   1 2 3 ④ 5

24

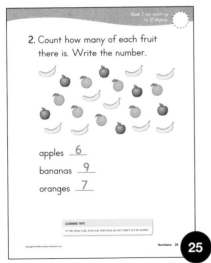

2. Count how many of each fruit there is. Write the number.

apples   6
bananas 9
oranges 7

25

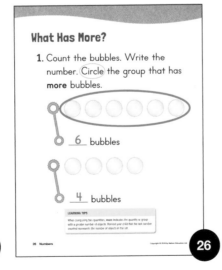

What Has More?

1. Count the bubbles. Write the number. Circle the group that has **more** bubbles.

6 bubbles

4 bubbles

26

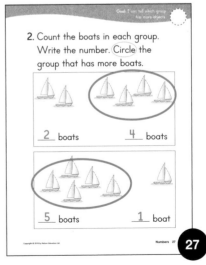

2. Count the boats in each group. Write the number. Circle the group that has more boats.

2 boats   4 boats

5 boats   1 boat

27

* Sample answer provided.

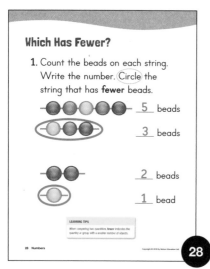

Which Has Fewer?

1. Count the beads on each string. Write the number. ⊂Circle⊃ the string that has **fewer** beads.

_5_ beads

_3_ beads

_2_ beads

_1_ bead

28 Numbers

Copyright © 2018 by Nelson Education Ltd.

28

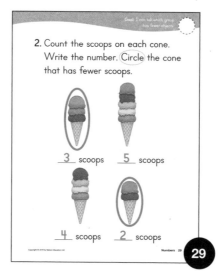

Goal: I can tell which group has fewer objects.

2. Count the scoops on each cone. Write the number. ⊂Circle⊃ the cone that has fewer scoops.

_3_ scoops   _5_ scoops

_4_ scoops   _2_ scoops

Copyright © 2018 by Nelson Education Ltd.   Numbers 29

29

More or Fewer?

1. Make pairs. Draw a line to match bunnies and carrots.

⊂Circle⊃ the group with more.

bunnies   carrots

30 Numbers

Copyright © 2018 by Nelson Education Ltd.

30

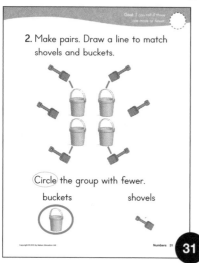

2. Make pairs. Draw a line to match shovels and buckets.

⊂Circle⊃ the group with fewer.

buckets   shovels

Copyright © 2018 by Nelson Education Ltd.   Numbers 31

31

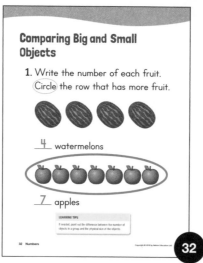

Comparing Big and Small Objects

1. Write the number of each fruit. ⊂Circle⊃ the row that has more fruit.

_4_ watermelons

_7_ apples

32 Numbers

Copyright © 2018 by Nelson Education Ltd.

32

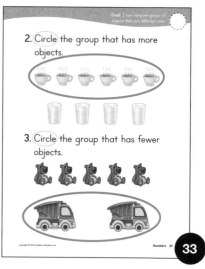

Goal: I can compare groups of objects that are different sizes.

2. ⊂Circle⊃ the group that has more objects.

3. ⊂Circle⊃ the group that has fewer objects.

Copyright © 2018 by Nelson Education Ltd.   Numbers 33

33

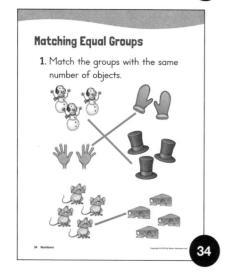

Matching Equal Groups

1. Match the groups with the same number of objects.

34 Numbers

Copyright © 2018 by Nelson Education Ltd.

34

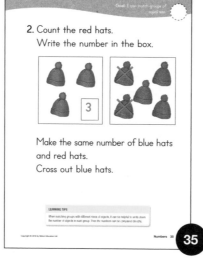

Goal: I can match groups of equal size.

2. Count the red hats. Write the number in the box.

3

Make the same number of blue hats and red hats.
Cross out blue hats.

Copyright © 2018 by Nelson Education Ltd.   Numbers 35

35

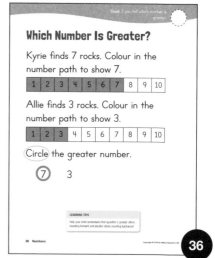

Goal: I can tell which number is greater.

Which Number Is Greater?

Kyrie finds 7 rocks. Colour in the number path to show 7.

| 1 | 2 | 3 | 4 | 5 | 6 | 7 | 8 | 9 | 10 |

Allie finds 3 rocks. Colour in the number path to show 3.

| 1 | 2 | 3 | 4 | 5 | 6 | 7 | 8 | 9 | 10 |

⊂Circle⊃ the greater number.

⑦   3

36 Numbers

Copyright © 2018 by Nelson Education Ltd.

36

---

* Sample answer provided.

Ordinal Numbers

The train has 5 cars.

How many windows does the second car have? __0__

How many windows does the third car have? __1__

Draw an X on the fourth car.

Circle the fifth car.

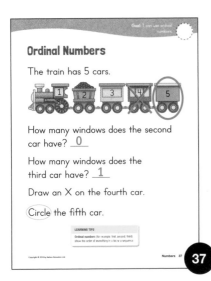

Coins

1. Match each coin to its name.

dime
quarter
loonie
nickel

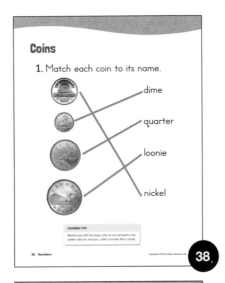

2. How much is each coin worth? Circle the value.

5¢ $1
25¢   **10¢**
25¢ 5¢
10¢   **$1**

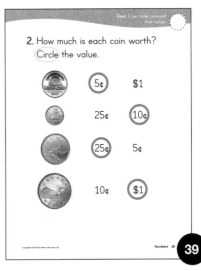

Taking Numbers Apart

There are 6 apples in a basket. Some are red. Some are yellow.

* 1. Colour the apples. Show how many are red and how many are yellow.

How many apples are red? __3__
How many apples are yellow? __3__
How many apples are there altogether? __6__

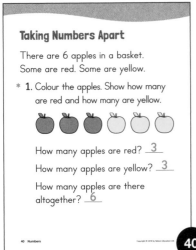

* 2. Colour the apples a different way. Show how many are red and how many are yellow.

How many apples are red? __4__
How many apples are yellow? __2__
How many apples are there altogether? __6__

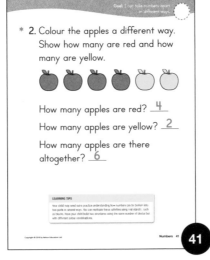

Putting Numbers Together

1. Count the total number of dots on each domino. Write the number below the domino.

__4__   __6__

__10__   __7__

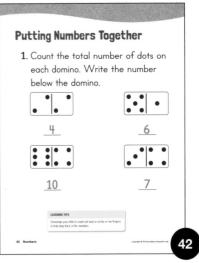

* Sample answer provided.

Answers   107

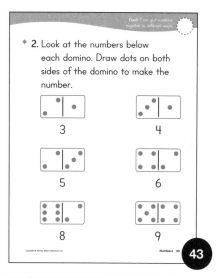

* 2. Look at the numbers below each domino. Draw dots on both sides of the domino to make the number.

3

4

5

6

8

9

Addition: 1 or 2 More

1. There are 4 frogs.

1 more frog comes along.

How many frogs are on the log now? 5

LEARNING TIPS

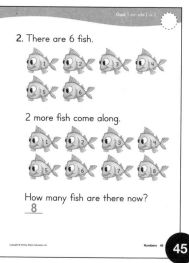

2. There are 6 fish.

2 more fish come along.

How many fish are there now? 8

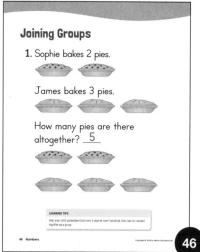

Joining Groups

1. Sophie bakes 2 pies.

James bakes 3 pies.

How many pies are there altogether? 5

LEARNING TIPS

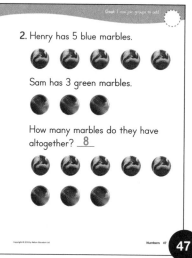

2. Henry has 5 blue marbles.

Sam has 3 green marbles.

How many marbles do they have altogether? 8

Subtraction: 1 or 2 Less

1. There are 4 birds on a branch.

1 bird flew away.

How many birds are on the branch now? 3

LEARNING TIPS

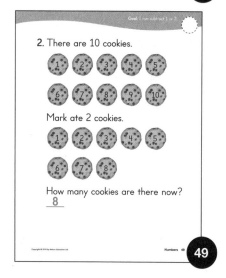

2. There are 10 cookies.

Mark ate 2 cookies.

How many cookies are there now? 8

Taking Groups Away

1. Gabriel has 6 cupcakes.

His friends eat the 3 blue cupcakes. Mark an X on the cupcakes his friends eat.

How many cupcakes are left? 3

LEARNING TIPS

2. Stella has 8 glasses of lemonade.

She sells the 5 glasses with lemon slices. Mark an X on the 5 glasses she sold.

How many glasses does she have left? 3

* Sample answer provided.

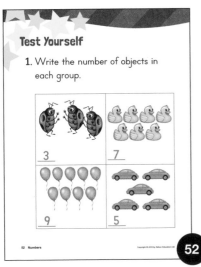

Test Yourself

1. Write the number of objects in each group.

3   7

9   5

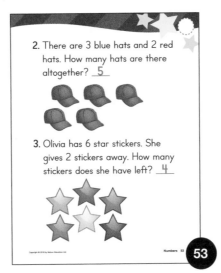

2. There are 3 blue hats and 2 red hats. How many hats are there altogether? __5__

3. Olivia has 6 star stickers. She gives 2 stickers away. How many stickers does she have left? __4__

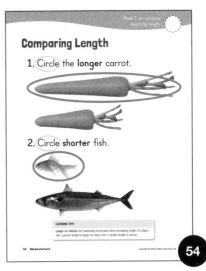

Comparing Length

1. Circle the **longer** carrot.

2. Circle **shorter** fish.

LEARNING TIPS
Longer and shorter are measuring terms used when comparing length. An object with a greater length is longer. An object with a smaller length is shorter.

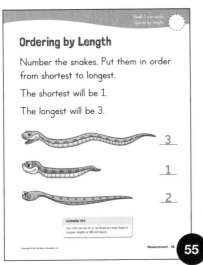

Ordering by Length

Number the snakes. Put them in order from shortest to longest.

The shortest will be 1.

The longest will be 3.

3

1

2

LEARNING TIPS
Your child can use his or her thumb and index finger to compare lengths of different objects.

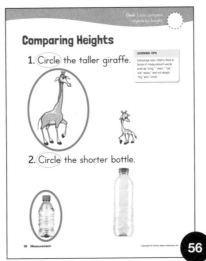

Comparing Heights

1. Circle the taller giraffe.

LEARNING TIPS
Encourage your child to think in terms of measurement words such as "long," "short," "tall," and "equal," and not simply "big" and "small."

2. Circle the shorter bottle.

Ordering by Height

Number the trees. Put them in order from shortest to tallest.

The shortest will be 1.

The tallest will be 3.

2   3   1

LEARNING TIPS
Tools such as pieces of string can be used to help compare heights or lengths of objects.

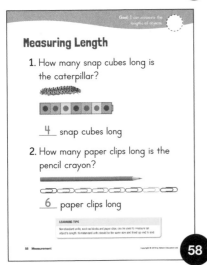

Measuring Length

1. How many snap cubes long is the caterpillar?

__4__ snap cubes long

2. How many paper clips long is the pencil crayon?

__6__ paper clips long

LEARNING TIPS
Non-standard units, such as blocks and paper clips, can be used to measure an object's length. Non-standard units should be the same size and lined up end to end.

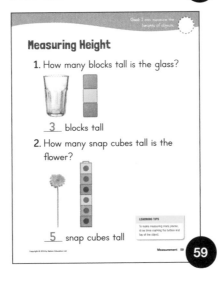

Measuring Height

1. How many blocks tall is the glass?

__3__ blocks tall

2. How many snap cubes tall is the flower?

__5__ snap cubes tall

LEARNING TIPS
To make measuring more precise, draw lines marking the bottom and top of the object.

Mass

1. Circle the heavier object.

2. Circle the lighter object.

LEARNING TIPS
Encourage your child to compare the mass of different objects by holding them. Ask them to tell you which one they think is heavier, and then have them hold the objects to see if they are correct.

* Sample answer provided.

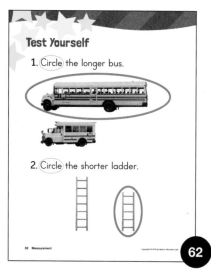

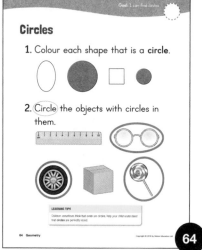

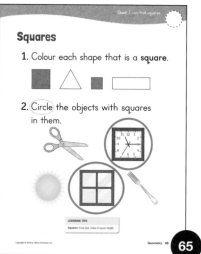

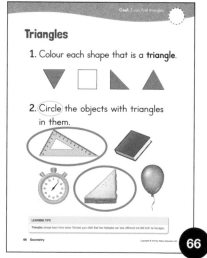

* Sample answer provided.

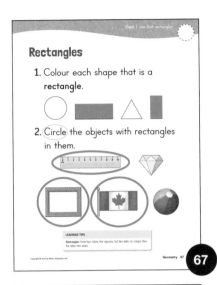

Rectangles

1. Colour each shape that is a **rectangle**.

2. Circle the objects with rectangles in them.

Geometry 67

67

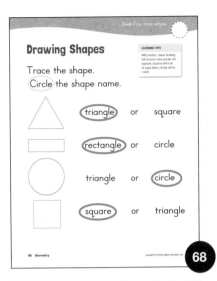

Drawing Shapes

LEARNING TIPS
With practice, shape drawing will become more precise. For example, squares will have all equal sides, circles will be round.

Trace the shape.
Circle the shape name.

triangle or square

rectangle or circle

triangle or circle

square or triangle

68 Geometry

68

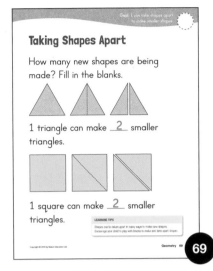

Taking Shapes Apart

How many new shapes are being made? Fill in the blanks.

1 triangle can make __2__ smaller triangles.

1 square can make __2__ smaller triangles.

LEARNING TIPS
Shapes can be taken apart in many ways to make new shapes. Encourage your child to play with shapes to make and take apart shapes.

Geometry 69

69

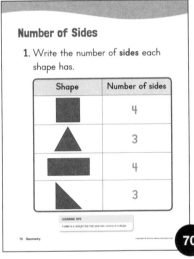

Number of Sides

1. Write the number of **sides** each shape has.

Shape	Number of sides
	4
	3
	4
	3

LEARNING TIPS
A side is a straight line that joins two corners of a shape.

70 Geometry

70

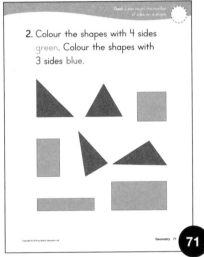

2. Colour the shapes with 4 sides green. Colour the shapes with 3 sides blue.

Geometry 71

71

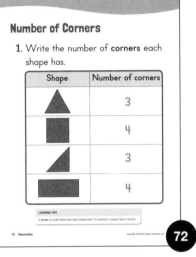

Number of Corners

1. Write the number of **corners** each shape has.

Shape	Number of corners
	3
	4
	3
	4

LEARNING TIPS
A corner is a point where two lines (sides) meet. For example, a square has 4 corners.

72 Geometry

72

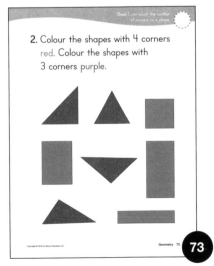

2. Colour the shapes with 4 corners red. Colour the shapes with 3 corners purple.

Geometry 73

73

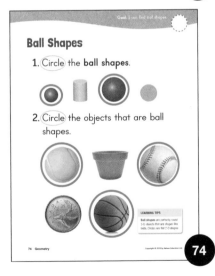

Ball Shapes

1. Circle the **ball shapes**.

2. Circle the objects that are ball shapes.

LEARNING TIPS
Ball shapes are perfectly round 3-D objects that are shaped like balls. Circles are flat 2-D shapes.

74 Geometry

74

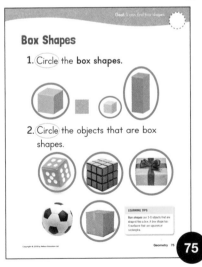

Box Shapes

1. Circle the **box shapes**.

2. Circle the objects that are box shapes.

LEARNING TIPS
Box shapes are 3-D objects that are shaped like a box. A box shape has 6 surfaces that are squares or rectangles.

Geometry 75

75

* Sample answer provided.

Answers 111

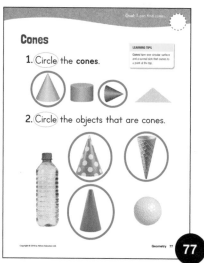

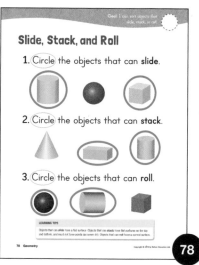

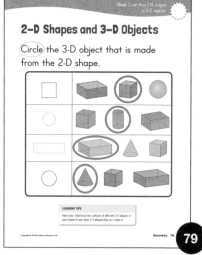

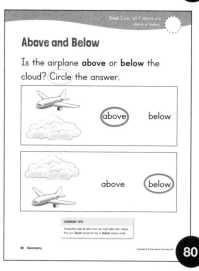

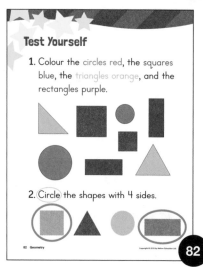

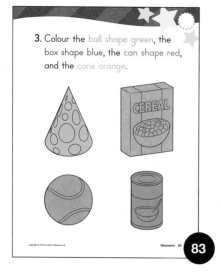

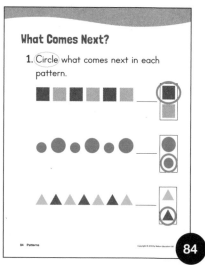

* Sample answer provided.

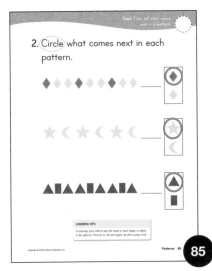

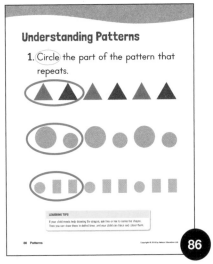

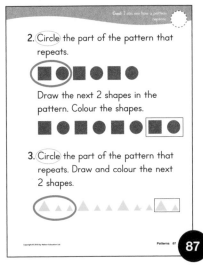

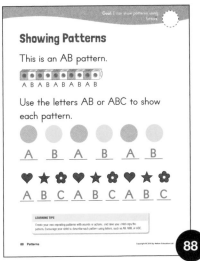

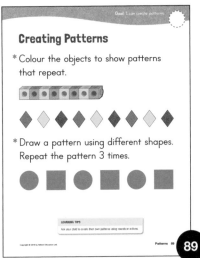

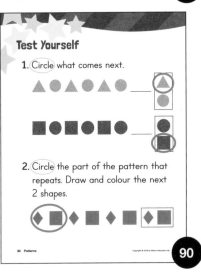

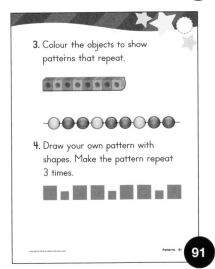

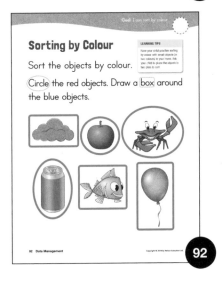

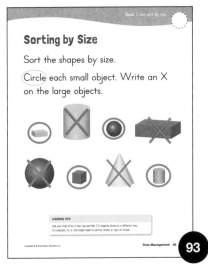

* Sample answer provided.

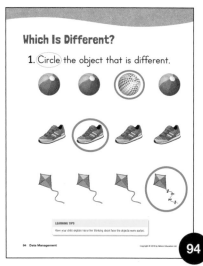

Which Is Different?

1. Circle the object that is different.

2. Write an X on the object that does not belong.

94

95

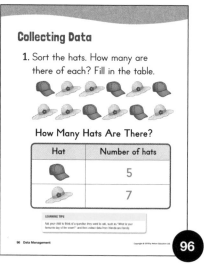

Collecting Data

1. Sort the hats. How many are there of each? Fill in the table.

How Many Hats Are There?

Hat	Number of hats
(cap)	5
(hat)	7

96

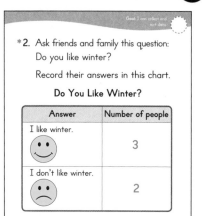

*2. Ask friends and family this question: Do you like winter?

Record their answers in this chart.

Do You Like Winter?

Answer	Number of people
I like winter. 😊	3
I don't like winter. 😐	2

97

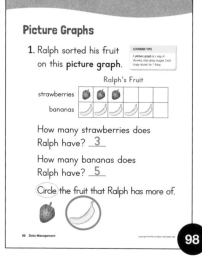

Picture Graphs

1. Ralph sorted his fruit on this **picture graph**.

Ralph's Fruit

strawberries / bananas

How many strawberries does Ralph have? __3__

How many bananas does Ralph have? __5__

Circle the fruit that Ralph has more of.

98

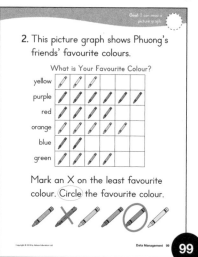

2. This picture graph shows Phuong's friends' favourite colours.

What is Your Favourite Colour?

yellow / purple / red / orange / blue / green

Mark an X on the least favourite colour. Circle the favourite colour.

99

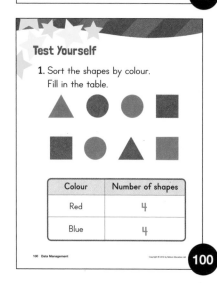

Test Yourself

1. Sort the shapes by colour. Fill in the table.

Colour	Number of shapes
Red	4
Blue	4

100

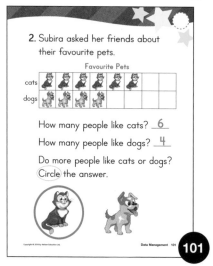

2. Subira asked her friends about their favourite pets.

Favourite Pets

cats / dogs

How many people like cats? __6__

How many people like dogs? __4__

Do more people like cats or dogs? Circle the answer.

101

* Sample answer provided.

COMPLETION CERTIFICATE

CONGRATULATIONS!

You have completed the Nelson Math Kindergarten Workbook!

Presented to:

_____

Date:

_____

GREAT JOB!